The Song of Wandering Aengus

William Butler Yeats

Illustrations by Marina Marcolin

I went out to the hazel wood,
Because a fire was in my head,

And cut and peeled a hazel wand,
And hooked a berry to a thread;

And when white moths were on the wing,
And moth-like stars were flickering out,
I dropped the berry in a stream
And caught a little silver trout.

When I had laid it on the floor
I went to blow the fire aflame
But something rustled on the floor,
And someone called me by my name:

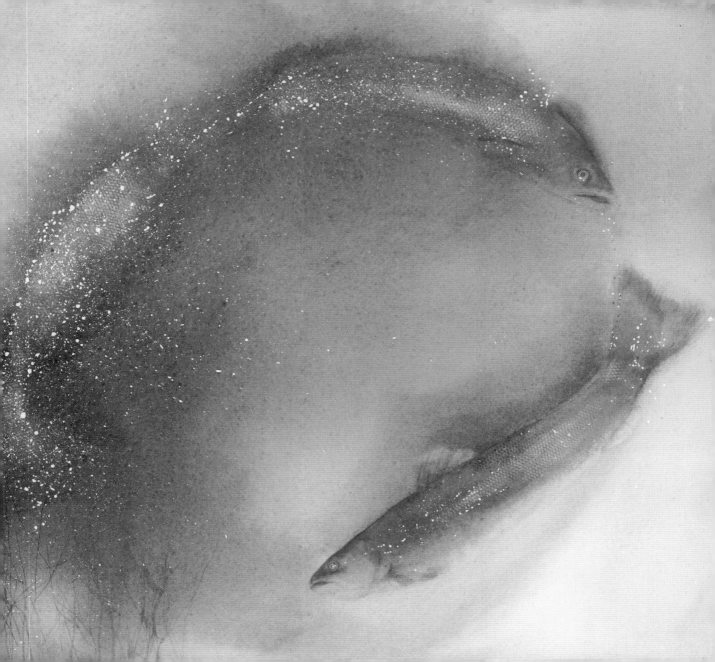

It had become a glimmering girl
With apple blossom in her hair
Who called me by my name and ran

And faded through the brightening air.

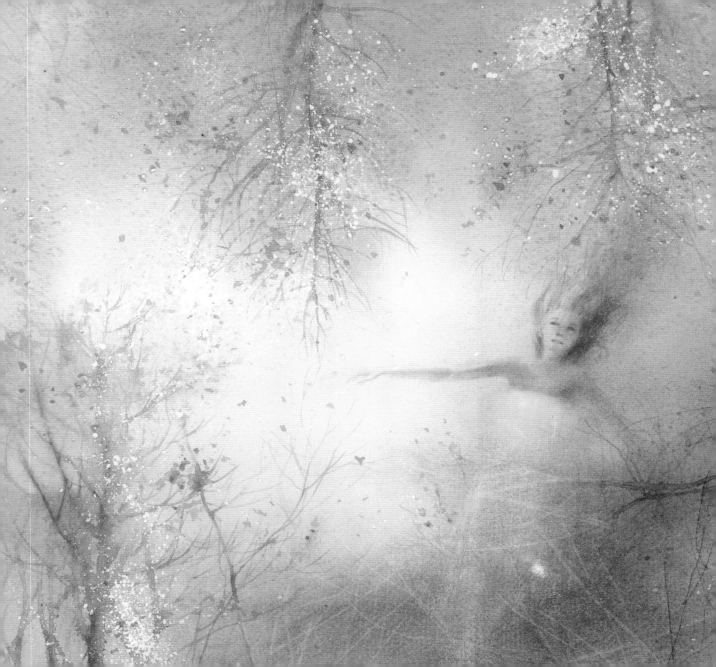

Though I am old with wandering

Through hollow lands and hilly lands,

I will find out where she has gone,
And kiss her lips and take her hands;

And walk among long dappled grass,

And pluck till time and times are done
The silver apples of the moon,
The golden apples of the sun.

The Song of Wandering Aengus

first appeared in 1899 in a collection titled *The Wind Among the Reeds*. It was published at a time of cultural innovation in Europe as writers and musicians became more and more aware of the traditional oral cultures of their native lands.

All across the continent, writers and composers such as the playwright Henrik Ibsen and composers such as Smetana, Dvorak and Greig were engaging with the folklore of their own people to create new work that expressed a sense of their national identities.

In Dublin, William Butler Yeats and his friends Lady Augusta Gregory, Douglas Hyde and others were also exploring their own native heritage of myths and stories and recreating them as plays and poems.

Aengus is a character of Irish mythology associated with lost love and yearning.

Yeats reworked the ancient story to express his own sense of loss – in 1889, he had proposed marriage to Maud Gonne, a young Dublin actress and feminist involved in the nationalist movement. She refused. Ten years later, Yeats proposed again and was once more turned down.

Two further attempts to persuade his love to be his bride were also rejected. The story of Yeats' love for Maud Gonne followed a pattern quite similar to that of the poem – she was never far from his thoughts all the rest of his life. Though they became close in later years, they never did get married.

By presenting his most personal feelings in the timeless voice of Aengus, the young poet created a lyric that continues to speak to us today.

To my father, Francesco — Marina

First published 2014 by Futa Fata
An Spidéal, Galway, Ireland

© 2014 Futa Fata

Illustrations © 2014 Marina Marcolin

Concept, Background Notes: Tadhg Mac Dhonnagáin.
Design: Karen Carty, Anú Design, Tara, County Meath.

ISBN: 978-1-906907-81-5